The boy and the tiger

A tiger lay in a cave.
It couldn't get up for it had
   a bad leg and it had a cut on
   its paw.

1

A boy ran into the cave.
He wanted to get out of the storm.
The boy could see the tiger and
  he was frightened.

But he could see the tiger had a bad paw.
It couldn't get up, so the boy
    was not frightened.

The boy looked at the bad leg.
He found a hook in the tiger's paw.
Round the hook the paw was red and raw.
The boy cut the hook out.

He put a rag round the leg.
The boy was cold and wet so he
   lay down by the tiger and
   went to sleep.

The boy's dad was a vet.
One day the boy was out with
   his dad and a man ran up.
'Come with me,' said the man.

The man took the boy and his dad to
  a tree.
There was a tiger in a net.
The tiger couldn't get out.

Some bad men had put up a net to
   get a tiger.
They wanted the tiger for a rug.

Dad put the tiger to sleep.
The men cut it down and pulled
   it out of the net.
The boy looked at it.

'It's the tiger I helped in
    the cave,' said the boy.
'We can let him go free,' said Dad.
'But not the bad men.'

Mad Mike

A mad man called Mike
   had a bike with a jet.
The bike went to Kent
   but Mike's not there yet.

The old jug

An old man lived with his son in
    a little house.
The son had no job and the old
    man couldn't see.

They were so poor they sold the
   pig and the hen.
In the end they had no food and
   they couldn't pay the rent.

One day the old man found a
gold pin in an old tin.
'My Meg gave me this pin on the
day we got wed,' he said.

The old man gave the pin to his son.
'Go to town,' he told him.
'Get what you can for it and we can
   get food and pay the rent.'

The son went to town and met an
  old woman.
She looked poor but she had
  things on a rug.

She told the son she had not had
   food for ten days.
'Help me, I beg,' she said.
'You poor old thing,' said the son.

The son gave the gold pin to
   the woman.
She gave him an old jug.
'This is for the pin,' she said.

The son told the old man about the
poor old woman.
The old man was cross.
'This old jug for a gold pin!' he said.

The son looked at the jug.
It said inside, 'I am a magic jug.'
'A magic jug!' said the son.
He gave the jug a rub.

'Zoom! Zip! Zam!
By the door was a little
    box of gold.
The old man was cross.

'We don't want a little bit of
   gold,' he said.
'What we want is a lot of it.'
He was so cross he hit his son.

But he hit the jug and down it went.
The jug was in bits.
'We won't get a lot of gold with
     the jug in bits,' said the son.

'But with this gold we can
    pay the rent.
We can get ten pigs and lots of hens.
We can get the house mended, and
    we won't be poor.'

24